HELLO!

This is your very own Achie
Check off each kitten y color

ASH BOLT CLEO DUKE ELMO FIZZ GIGI

HUGO IVY JAZZ KIKI NEMO LULU PIP

MILO QUIN OPAL REX UMA SKY FLORA

AXEL VIVI WIZZ YUKI ALFI BEA FINN

COCO STAIN EVE GUS HALO KAI IRIS

OZZY JOJO LEX MIA POE NYX QUIP

RUBY SID TIA UDO VEX WOLF

XIO YALE DEZI TOBY

I'm Ash! My fur is like silver

BOLT

I'm Bolt! Faster than the wind

I'm Cleo!
Royal blood runs through me

DUKE
I'm Duke! Born to lead

I’m Elmo! I adore hugs

I'm Fizz! Can't sit still

I'm Gigi!
Bright and elegant

I'm Hugo! I love to ponder

I'm Ivy! Climbing high

JAZZ

I'm Jazz!
My song is in purring

KIKI
I'm Kiki!
A bundle of joy

I'm Nemo!
The ocean explorer

I'm Lulu!
The embodiment of calmness

I'm Pip! A master of stealth

I’m Milo!
Living for adventures

I'm Quin! Full of surprises

I'm Opal! I change color in the sun

I'm Rex!
An explorer of hideouts

I'm Uma! Unique and bright

SKY
I'm Sky!
Dreaming, looking
out the window

FLORA

AXEL
I'm Axel!
Strength in every move

VIVI
I'm Vivi! Life is my stage

WIZZ

I'm Wizz!
Sparkling with ideas

YUKI

I'm Yuki!
Fluffy like the first snow

I'm Alfi!
A prankster and mischief-maker

BEA
I'm Bea!
Dreaming under the starlight

FINN
I'm Finn! Sea breeze

I’m Coco!
Guardian of the cookie jar

STAIN

I'm Stain! Smarter than all

EVE
I'm Eve!
I shine with the brightness of day

I'm Gus! I radiate kindness

HALO

I'm Halo! Cozy home comfort

I'm Kai!
The wind plays in my fur

I’m Iris!
Home among the flowers

OZZY
I'm Ozzy! A wizard of joy

I'm Jojo! Life is a game

I'm Lex! Wisdom in a glance

I'm Mia! A ray of sunshine

I'm Poe! I inspire with tales

I'm Nyx! Full of mysteries

I'm Quip! Wit is my gift

RUBY
I'm Ruby!
A treasure of the home

SID
I'm Sid!
A curious explorer

TIA
I'm Tia!
The warmth of family

UDO
I'm Udo!
Unique in every step

VEX
I'm Vex!
Caprices are my art

WOLF

I'm Wolf! Wild and free

XIO
I'm Xio!
A mystery in every purr

YALE

I'm Yale!
Seeking knowledge everywhere

DEZI
I'm Dezi! Always looking for new friends

TOBY
I'm Toby!
Playing until sunset

MEOW

Made in United States
Troutdale, OR
12/09/2024